A Note to Parents

Eyewitness Readers is a compell[ing new reading?]
programme for children. *Eyewit[ness has become the]*
most trusted name in illustrated books, and this new
series combines the highly visual *Eyewitness* approach
with engaging, easy-to-read stories. Each *Eyewitness
Reader* is guaranteed to capture a child's interest while
developing his or her reading skills, general knowledge
and love of reading.

The books are written by leading children's authors
and are designed in conjunction with literacy experts,
including Cliff Moon M.Ed., Honorary Fellow of the
University of Reading. Cliff Moon spent many years as
a teacher and teacher educator specializing in reading.
He has written more than 140 books for children and
teachers, and he reviews regularly for teachers' journals.

The four levels of *Eyewitness Readers* are aimed at
different reading abilities, enabling you to choose the
books that are exactly right for each child.

Level 1 – Beginning to read
Level 2 – Beginning to read alone
Level 3 – Reading alone
Level 4 – Proficient readers

The "normal" age at which a
child begins to read can be
anywhere from three to eight
years old, so these levels are
only guidelines.

No matter which level you select,
you can be sure that you're
helping children learn to read,
then read to learn!

DK

A Dorling Kindersley Book
www.dk.com

Created by Leapfrog Press Ltd

Project Editor Elizabeth Bacon
Art Editor Andrew Burgess

For Dorling Kindersley
Senior Editor Linda Esposito
Senior Art Editor Diane Thistlethwaite
Production Josie Alabaster
Picture Researcher Liz Moore
Illustrator Peter Dennis

Reading Consultant
Cliff Moon M.Ed.

Published in Great Britain by
Dorling Kindersley Limited
9 Henrietta Street
London WC2E 8PS

4 6 8 10 9 7 5 3

Eyewitness Readers™ is a trademark of
Dorling Kindersley Limited, London.

Text copyright © 1999 David Clement-Davies
Illustration and compilation copyright © 1999 Dorling Kindersley Limited, London

Colour reproduction by Colourscan, Singapore
Printed and bound in Belgium by Proost

The publisher would like to thank the following
for their kind permission to reproduce their photographs:
Key: t=top, a=above, b=below, l=left, r=right, c=centre

AKG UK Ltd: 4bl, 6tl; Ancient Art & Architecture: 8tl, 11br, 42tl
/John King: 21tr /Ronald Sheridan: 21br; Bridgeman Art Library:
12br, 18tl, 25br, 37tc, 42bl, 46tlc; Andrew Burgess: 40tl; Bruce Coleman Ltd:
17tr, 28tl; Dorling Kindersley Picture Library: 7cr, 8bl, 10tl, b, 11tr, 13 all,
26b, 32bl, 34cl cla; /British Museum: 7tr, 24tl, 32tl, 33tr, 35cr, 42cl, 46tl;
/Church's Ministry Among the Jews: 16tr, /Steve Gorton 39br;
/Frank Greenaway: 39tr; /Bob Langrish/Mrs J Quinny: 28bl; /Natural History
Museum/Colin Keates: 39cr; /Natural History Museum/Harry Taylor:
46tlb; /Nick Nicholls: 13br, 18bl, 32tl, 32-33b, 33tr, 35cr, 37tr;
Clive Streeter: 37br; Mary Evans Picture Library: 4tl, 30tl;
/Garden Picture Library: 38tl; Sonia Halliday: 15br, 19tr,
44tl, 47tr; Robert Harding Picture Library: 5br, 12tl, 40bl, 46bl;
Michael Holford: 36bl; Images Colour Library: 15tr;
Jeff Moore: 27br; Science Photo Library: 24bl

The publisher would also like to thank
the London Lyceum of Greek Women
for their kind help.

Contents

TROJAN HORSE

THE WORLD'S GREATEST ADVENTURE

Written by David Clement-Davies

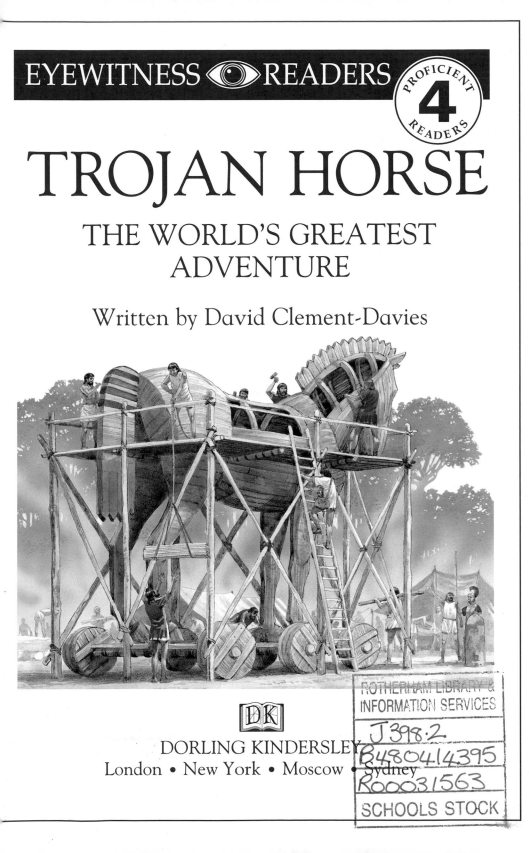

DK

DORLING KINDERSLEY

London • New York • Moscow • Sydney

Homer
Some historians think that Homer was blind. Others question if he lived at all.

Trojan mask
The ruins of ancient Troy were found in the late 19th century. Many treasures, including this gold mask, were dug up there.

Legends and heroes

About 2,700 years ago, when Greece was one of the greatest civilizations in the world, the Greek writer Homer wrote two poems, *The Iliad* (ill-ee-ad) and *The Odyssey* (odd-i-see). The poems told the story of a war between Greece and Troy 500 years before Homer lived. They were based on Greek history and legends.

Troy was a large walled city in what is now Turkey. Homer told how the Greeks tried to capture it for ten years, then thought up a clever scheme to invade the city by using a giant wooden horse.

The ancient Greeks prayed to many gods, called immortals. They built temples for their gods and offered them harvest fruits and animal sacrifices.

In the poems, the most important gods help start the war and interfere in the plan for the wooden horse.

EASTERN EUROPE

Black Sea

ITALY

• Mount Olympus

• Mount Ida

GREECE   *Aegean Sea*   Troy

Ithaca •

TURKEY

Mediterranean Sea

Sparta •

CRETE

———————— The Greeks' route to Troy

The gods in this story include Zeus, king of the gods; his queen, Hera; and two of his daughters, Aphrodite and Athena. They discuss the war in heaven, then use magical powers to protect their favourite humans and punish their enemies.

The Iliad and *The Odyssey* are two of the world's best-known poems. This retelling includes some of the most exciting adventures in a magical tale of love and hate, power and revenge, gods and heroes.

Mount Olympus (o-lim-puss) In Greek myth, this was the home of the gods, including Zeus (z-yooss), Hera (hear-ah), Aphrodite (aff-ro-die-tee) and Athena.

5

The golden apple

All day long the gods feasted on Mount Olympus. They ate fabulous foods and drank from golden cups brimming with nectar.

Hera, queen of the gods, had invited all but one of the gods to the feast. She had not invited the goddess Spite, because Spite started arguments and created misery wherever she went.

Heavenly drink
Nectar is the sweet liquid in flowers that bees make into honey. The gods drank nectar from golden cups.

Suddenly Spite appeared and stood glaring at the guests.

"Here is my gift to you," she cried and threw a golden apple into the middle of the party.

On the apple were the words "FOR THE MOST BEAUTIFUL".

Hera snatched up the apple.

"I am queen of the gods!" she cried. "I must be the most beautiful. The apple is mine."

But Athena, the goddess of wisdom, disagreed.

"No, Hera, you are wrong," she said. "The apple belongs to me."

Then Aphrodite sidled in between them.

"I am the goddess of love and beauty," she sighed. "Surely the apple is mine."

A quarrel broke out between the proud goddesses, though each was more beautiful than any woman on earth. The happy day was ruined.

Goddesses
Each goddess controlled a different aspect of human life and had a symbol to represent the aspect. Queen Hera's symbol was a peacock – a royal bird.

Athena
An owl symbolized the goddess of wisdom and warfare.

Aphrodite
A red rose symbolized the goddess of love.

Flock of sheep
Since ancient times, Greek shepherds have herded sheep and goats for milk, cheese and wool.

Twin pipes
Ancient Greeks played two pipes at a time. Pipes were made from sycamore wood.

Zeus, king of the gods, grew tired of the goddesses' quarrelling. He sent them to see a shepherd named Paris, who lived on Mount Ida near the city of Troy. Paris was famous for his good judgment.

Paris was playing his pipes in the morning sunlight when the goddesses appeared before him.

He was dumbstruck at the sight of the three dazzling immortals.

Hera placed the golden apple on the dewy grass.

"This apple is for the most beautiful goddess. Zeus commands you to choose which one of us deserves it," she said. "If you give it to me, I will give you as much power on earth as Zeus has in heaven."

Then bright-eyed Athena spoke, "If you give me the prize, I will make you the wisest man in the world and the winner of every battle."

Then Aphrodite smiled, and Paris was nearly blinded by her beauty.

"Paris, if you give me the prize, you shall have Helen, a daughter of Zeus. She is as beautiful as I am."

Without a second thought, Paris took the apple and handed it to Aphrodite. The goddesses vanished. But not before Paris had made two very powerful enemies.

Paris and Helen

Soon after, King Priam of Troy decided to hold a sports contest in memory of a baby son who had died. He sent his servants to Mount Ida to capture a bull for first prize.

Paris heard the servants talking. The thought of being champion of Priam's games thrilled him. He left the peace of Mount Ida and went down into the bustling city of Troy.

The strong young shepherd showed his skill in every event.

Royal beast
A bull was thought to be king of the beasts. Bulls were often used as sports prizes.

Pentathletes
Like Paris, athletes often competed in a pentathlon, a contest of five events.

He won two throwing contests and the jumping, wrestling and running competitions, even beating the royal princes.

Hector, the eldest prince, drew his sword to kill the shepherd who dared challenge him. Just then, an old man threw himself at King Priam's feet.

"My lord!" he cried. "This is no ordinary shepherd. This is the beloved son in whose memory you are holding these games."

Priam was amazed.

"Remember when your son was born?" the old man asked. "Your wife dreamt that he would cause the destruction of Troy. I am the servant you ordered to leave the baby on Mount Ida to die. But I took pity on the child. I nursed him and watched him grow up into a fine young man."

Priam was overjoyed that he had found his son again. He gave Paris his rightful place as a prince of Troy.

Wreath
Men honoured the gods by holding sporting events. Winners were given a laurel wreath to wear. The laurel is the holy tree of the god Apollo.

Chilly peaks
The mountains near Troy reached up to 3,000 metres (9,842 feet) high. Wolves and other wild animals roamed there.

Ancient Sparta
The powerful Greek city of Sparta was ruled by a king. Spartan people excelled in arts and war.

Sailing ships
Homer called Greek ships "beaked" because they had long thin fronts, often decorated with birds' heads. The fronts could ram enemy ships.

That night, Paris woke suddenly. Before him stood Aphrodite, bathed in moonlight. She whispered, "Helen is the queen of Sparta. Go there and find her, Paris. Remember, I will always look after you, for you gave the golden apple to me."

The next day Paris tied a silver statue of Aphrodite to his ship's mast, because the goddess of love had sworn to protect him. He set sail across the glittering seas and soon arrived in Sparta. When he caught sight of Helen, she was so beautiful that he immediately fell in love.

Paris brought greetings from Priam and sweet perfumes for Helen. Her husband, King Menelaus (men-e-lay-uss), welcomed Paris into his fine palace. His slaves bathed Paris and dressed him in a purple robe.

Then they led Paris to a chamber where his royal hosts were waiting. A magnificent feast was laid out.

Goat's cheese

Bread with goat's cheese

Bread

Olives

Figs

Fish

Wine cup

Grapes

But Paris was not interested in food. All evening he watched Helen. He longed to be with her at any cost, even though she was the wife of Menelaus, noble king of Sparta.

As the feast ended, Paris spilled his wine on the supper table. In the blood-red liquid he traced the words "I love you" for only Helen to see.

Wine and dine
Fish, cheese, fruit and wine were served at a feast. Meat was eaten only on religious occasions.

13

Night fell. Only Paris and Helen stayed awake, and they sat talking quietly. Now Aphrodite wove her powerful magic for Paris and made Helen fall in love with him.

Paris took Helen's hand and led her out of the silent palace to his waiting ship. They set sail back to Troy, across the moonlit sea.

The goddess Hera still hated Paris for not giving her the apple. She sent wild storms to wreck Paris's ship, but Aphrodite made sure that he reached Troy unharmed.

The Trojans gave their prince a joyful welcome home. Only the prophetess Cassandra, Priam's daughter, was unhappy to see Helen.

She warned the people that Helen would bring disaster on Troy, but none of the Trojans believed her.

Aphrodite's spell slowly wore off Helen. Alone in her chamber, the queen wept for what she had done.

Danger at sea
The Aegean (i-gee-an) Sea between Sparta in Greece and Troy in Turkey is often stormy.

Prophets
People who predicted the future were called prophets (proff-itts). They were often priests. Greeks visited temples where they asked for prophecies from the priests.

15

When the sun rose over Sparta the next day, Menelaus stormed through his palace. In the night he had dreamt that Paris was going to steal Helen. Then Menelaus awoke to discover that it was true! He found Paris's purple robe and tore it in two.

"I call on you gods to help me get revenge on Paris!" he roared to the skies. Athena heard his prayer and smiled. She would help him, for Paris was her enemy, too.

Menelaus needed men to sail to Troy with him to win back Helen. The king sent messengers to the rulers of Greece.

From every island and mountaintop kings and princes journeyed to Sparta with soldiers.

Two great warriors joined the Greek army: Odysseus (odd-i-see-us), king of Ithaca, and Prince Achilles (a-kill-ees), the son of a sea goddess.

A magnificent fleet of one thousand ships set sail for Troy. The sun god Apollo blew a gentle wind to speed their voyage and told dolphins to leap the waves.

Dolphins
Sailors believed that Apollo commanded the dolphins and that they were safe if dolphins followed them.

Fine fast fleets
Greek warships were light and fast. Each had a big linen sail and was rowed by 50 oarsmen.

Sword

Spear-head

War weapons
Soldiers carried bronze weapons such as swords and spears. They wore bronze helmets which were embossed, or decorated.

Helmet

The war begins

The ships sailed for nearly three weeks, through black storms one minute, under blue skies the next, for the gods were arguing. Zeus sent down thunder and lightning to please Aphrodite. Then Apollo blew the storm clouds away and calmed the winds, which delighted Athena.

At last the fleet landed on the shores of Troy. An angry swarm of Trojans immediately attacked the soldiers. Achilles led the Greeks into the first battle. Both sides fought ferociously. Swords sparked and clashed in the midday sun.

Achilles fought with such skill that the Trojans lost courage and fled back inside the walls of Troy. They barred the heavy city gates.

Odysseus and Menelaus went to talk calmly to Priam and demand Helen's return. The old king listened to the noble leaders.

But the Trojan people were in no mood for peace and they turned violently on Odysseus and Menelaus. The two heroes only just escaped. Furious, the Greeks declared war.

On the plain outside the city and along the shore where their ships were anchored, the Greeks put up their tents. That night the shore was lit with hundreds of flickering campfires.

Plain of Troy The flat plain between Troy and the sea was about 2.5 kilometres (1.6 miles) wide.

The Trojans stayed safe behind their high city walls, and try as they might, the Greeks could not capture the city. They gave up trying to smash down the walls. Instead, they surrounded Troy and attacked the nearby villages. The siege continued for days and months and then years.

In the tenth year, a terrible argument broke out between Achilles and a noble Greek commander. They fought bitterly over who should own a beautiful slave girl.

"I'll never fight the Trojans with you again!" Achilles swore to the commander. "Even if you beg me on your knees to help you!"

Achilles strode back to his tent and ripped off his armour in a rage.

It was up to Odysseus to rally the weary Greeks.

"Come, brave warriors, we can still win Helen and conquer Troy without Achilles," he cried. "Ten long years have passed and now it is time for victory!"

The soldiers cheered and took up their weapons. They marched onto the great plain and waited.

The Trojans saw that Achilles was not leading his army. They no longer had to fear him! Their great warrior, Hector, led his charioteers out of the city. Dust clouds flew up as horses' hooves and chariot wheels thundered across the dark plain of Troy.

A duel for peace

The two armies met on the battle plain. Hector and his Trojans advanced with war cries, while the Greeks moved forwards in grim silence to meet their enemy.

The armies were on the brink of battle when Paris rode out from the Trojan ranks and faced the Greeks.

"I challenge any Greek to a duel, man to man!" he shouted boldly. "The winner shall have Helen and this long war will end."

Menelaus, hungry for revenge, leapt down from his bronze chariot.

"Paris, you miserable thief!" he cried. "I will fight you!"

Paris was terrified that his arch-rival had taken up the challenge. Trembling, he backed away.

Hector persuaded his cowardly brother to fight.

"Paris, for once act like an honourable man. Remember, lovely Helen will be in the high tower watching you. Fight for her like a hero."

So Paris and Menelaus took up their weapons. First Paris hurled his spear at Menelaus, but he missed. Menelaus sprang towards Paris, grabbed him by the throat and dragged him towards the Greek lines.

Athena hovered above Menelaus. Her steely eyes flashed with triumph.

At that moment Aphrodite flew down, hid her beloved Paris in a mist, and spirited him away from the battlefield.

But Menelaus had won the duel and peace was declared at last.

Wine cup
The gods were served nectar by a male or female servant called a cupbearer.

God speed
A meteor is a rock-like object that shoots from outer space through the sky. Several other gods besides Athena were said to travel as forces of nature. For example, Zeus travelled as a thunderbolt.

On Mount Olympus, Hera and Athena stood glaring at Zeus, who was sipping red nectar.

"Well," Zeus mocked the two angry goddesses, "Aphrodite is working hard to protect her Trojan prince. What are you two doing for the Greeks? Perhaps you are both happy now that peace has been declared between the two armies?"

Hera stamped her foot in rage and yelled at her husband, "How dare you say that! This war should go on until the Greeks conquer Troy. Zeus, let Athena ruin the peace between the Greeks and the Trojans!"

There was silence. Then Zeus sighed, "Very well. Send my warrior child to stir up the war again."

Athena dived from heaven, disguised as a blazing meteor.

Her fiery spirit seized the heart of a Trojan soldier and made him long to kill a Greek leader and be a hero.

"Forget peace," he thought. "I will fight for my city and my king."

Menelaus stood near the gates of Troy. The young Trojan crept up behind him and held a spear ready to strike. Menelaus heard a noise, swung around, and the Trojan fled.

The precious peace was broken. The furious Greek army turned on the Trojans, and battle cries echoed across the plain once more.

Shields were made from layers of animal skin, or hide, edged in bronze.

25

Man in charge
Families were ruled by the men and a baby boy was valued more than a baby girl.

Clothing
Greek males wore cloaks over knee-length tunics called chitons (kie-tons). Women wore full-length chitons.

Hector, Trojan hero

That night, outside the royal palace, Hector stood surrounded by his soldiers. They were pleading with him, "Hector, how can we force back the angry Greeks? Show us how to fight them!"

Hector was silent. He looked up at the stars. Then he left his men and went inside the palace to see his family.

He threw off his red cloak and put on his armour. His wife looked at him with fear in her dark eyes. She was certain he was going to die in battle.

Hector knelt down to kiss his son but the baby was terrified of his father's shining helmet with its horns and horsehair plume.

Hector laughed and took off the helmet. He lifted his son high and said,

"Little one, as lovely as a star, one day you will be a brave Trojan hero!"

Hector told his wife, "The gods give me no choice. I must fight to the death, my love."

In battle, Hector fought so bravely that the Greeks soon fled in terror towards the shore. Then the Trojans started to set fire to the Greek ships.

Without Achilles the Greeks were lost. Patroclus, Achilles' best friend and cousin, raced to the hero's tent.

"Achilles, we are in danger! Let me wear your armour," he begged. "I will fool the Trojans into thinking I am you. They will retreat in panic."

Achilles agreed, but warned him, "Patroclus, do not try to capture Troy alone. If you do, you will anger Apollo, who now loves the Trojans!"

Trojan torch
Soldiers used burning torches to set fire to enemy ships. The light warships were made of quick-burning wood.

Vulture
People believed
the gods could
change into
different forms.
Athena, war
goddess, turned
into this bird of
prey, which suits
her nature.

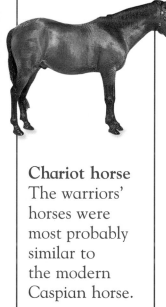

Chariot horse
The warriors'
horses were
most probably
similar to
the modern
Caspian horse.

Dressed as Achilles, Patroclus led the Greek army out to fight the Trojans.

Athena disguised herself as a vulture, and watched from the top of a tall pine tree. Apollo stood on the walls of Troy, robed in sunlight.

When the Trojans saw Patroclus, their hearts sank. They thought Achilles had returned to fight! They stumbled over one another in terror as they tried to escape his spear.

Many Trojan heroes were killed, and the rest scattered in front of Patroclus. Even mighty Hector leapt into his chariot and wheeled it round, shouting to the Trojans to run for the gates of Troy.

But Patroclus was far too bold. He forgot Achilles' warning and raced towards Troy on his own.

Apollo saw the hero trying to scale the city walls. The furious god flung him down onto his chariot.

Then Apollo shot a ray of sun to blind Patroclus's horse. It reared in fright and Patroclus tumbled from his chariot. His helmet flew from his head and his spear broke into pieces.

Hector shouted to the Trojans, "It was a trick! This is not Achilles!"

As Patroclus tried to crawl away, Hector killed him with a single blow. He stripped Achilles' armour from the dead body. Then, with a war cry, Hector led the Trojan army back into the heat of battle.

Sun god
Apollo is the gods' archer, who uses rays of the sun as golden arrows. He is often shown riding a golden chariot across the sky.

Hard hitter
The blacksmith of the gods was also the god of fire. He forged fine metal objects for the gods. For example, he made shoes for Apollo's horses.

River Styx
The Greeks believed that the Styx (sticks) divided the land of the living from Hades (hay-dees), the kingdom of the dead.

Death of the heroes

A messenger ran to tell Achilles that Hector had killed Patroclus and taken his armour. Achilles cried out so loudly that his mother, the sea goddess Thetis, heard him from her sea cave and sped to her son's side.

"Mother," he wept, "help me to avenge my beloved friend's death!"

That night on Mount Olympus, Thetis asked the blacksmith of the gods to make her son a brand-new suit of armour. The god set to work, surrounded by fire and steam.

In the pale dawn, Thetis, cloaked in silvery mist, carried a gleaming helmet and shield to Achilles.

"My son," Thetis whispered, "listen carefully. When you were a baby I dipped you in the River Styx whose waters give everlasting life to those who touch them.

"But your heel stayed dry. If your heel is wounded you will die."

Achilles put on the golden helmet and took the mighty shield. He went to the walls of Troy and called on Hector to fight him.

The air rang with the sound of clashing swords and spears. Hector fought well, but try as he might, he could not pierce Achilles' magical armour. At last Achilles thrust his long spear into Hector's neck.

Then Achilles tore off Hector's armour and tied the hero's body to the back of his golden chariot.

Three times Achilles circled Troy in his chariot, while old King Priam and the Trojans watched in horror from the city walls.

Plain cruelty
The bodies of those who died in battle were treated with respect. Achilles' cruelty was shocking.

Oil flask

Last respects
A hero's body was covered in oil and wrapped in cloth before burning.

Buried treasure
Most people were buried with their treasures.

Achilles kept Hector's body tied to his chariot. Day after day Achilles dragged the broken body round the city walls. He refused to return the dead hero to grieving Priam.

The gods grew angry, because the body of a hero must be burnt if his soul is to find rest. Even Thetis could not reason with her stubborn son.

One night King Priam visited Achilles in his tent and begged for his son's body. Priam's grief touched Achilles' heart. He agreed to return Hector's body but only in exchange for Hector's weight in gold.

Achilles built a giant pair of scales outside Troy. On one side the Greeks laid Hector's body. On the other side the Trojans placed all of Priam's gold. But Hector's body was still heavier than the treasure.

Cassandra, Hector's sister, leant out from the high walls of Troy and took off her golden bracelet. She dropped it onto the gold. It tipped the balance. The body rose as the gold sank to the ground.

The Trojans lifted the body over the walls and built a funeral pyre.

Old gold
Ancient kings collected gold objects and money. Coins were introduced into ancient Greece in about 700 BC from Turkey.

Procession
A hero's funeral was a major event. Mourners, dressed in black, carried the body to the funeral pyre, where the body was burnt. The women cut their hair as a sign of respect.

Hemlock leaves and flower

Poison arrow
Arrows were dipped in powerful poisons such as the juices of the hemlock plant. This caused a slow and very painful death.

The terrible siege went on and on. Achilles still wore his magical armour and no one could beat him.

But one day the warrior made a foolish boast on the battle plain.

"Look how strong I am," he cried. "I could even beat the gods!"

The god Apollo was looking down from Mount Olympus.

"It is time to punish Achilles; his vanity insults the gods," he thought.

Paris had also seen Achilles. He put a poisoned arrow to his bow, took aim, and fired from the walls.

Apollo turned the wind and blew the arrow straight towards Achilles' foot. The arrow pierced the hero's heel, the only weak part of his body. He gasped and fell. The arrow's deadly poison flowed through his strong veins. Slowly, and in terrible pain, the mighty Greek warrior died.

The Greeks could not believe that their great Achilles was dead.

They burnt his body in front of the city. Thetis, heartbroken, carried her son's soul up to heaven.

Paris bragged of his skill in killing the hero, but he grew careless too. One day a Greek archer spotted Paris on the city walls and shot three poisoned arrows at him, fatally wounding him. Paris was dead, but the city of Troy had not yet fallen.

Medical model The part of the heel that is easily injured is called the Achilles' tendon, after the ancient Greek hero's fatal weak spot.

Slaves
Greek society depended on slaves, people who had no freedom. Slaves were put to work as miners, servants and teachers.

Could the Greeks conquer Troy now that Achilles was dead?

Odysseus, the cleverest of all the Greeks, had a brilliant idea. But first he wanted to spy on the Trojans and find out everything about their city.

He disguised himself as a runaway slave, then slipped through Troy's gates into the wide streets.

Near Priam's palace he mingled with the crowds and watched the Trojan guards on the city walls. Helen caught sight of him from the palace gateway.

Her heart leapt for joy when she recognized brave Odysseus. She waved to him to come into the palace.

This is part of a palace of ancient Greece. Priam's palace in Troy may have looked the same.

Helen led him to her private chamber. She whispered to him, "Odysseus, I am a prisoner here. Hector was my only friend and now he is dead. And his poor father, who is kind to me, still weeps. I do not miss Paris, but I mourn our great Achilles!"

Helen showed Odysseus the loom where every day she sat alone and wove pictures of the war and of her long-lost homeland of Sparta.

The pictures on the beautiful purple cloth reminded Odysseus of the family he had left in Ithaca and, for a while, he was sad. Then he spoke:

"Listen, dear Helen, I know how we can win this war and take you back to Menelaus and your country."

He told her his plan and swore her to secrecy. Helen gladly told him all she knew about the city. Then she bathed him and brought him wine.

Much later, Odysseus left her and crept silently out of Troy.

Looms
Every Greek woman could make cloth. Mothers taught their daughters how to spin wool and weave it on a loom.

Bath oil
Greek house guests were rubbed with olive oil and perfume after taking a bath.

Timber!
Pine trees can grow very tall in the wild. They have always been valued for their timber.

The wooden horse

The next day at the Greek camp the leaders listened to Odysseus's plan. They all agreed it was excellent.

Odysseus took a shipbuilder and two other men to help him cut down fifty giant pine trees in the forest.

The Greeks used some of the trees to build a high wall on the plain. Hidden from sight behind the wall, they set to work.

They built a giant wooden horse, so big that thirty men could hide in the hollow middle.

The Greek soldiers worked fast and by evening the horse was ready.

Its mane and tail were painted purple and gold, and its eyes sparkled with purple gems. Under its legs were huge wooden wheels. It was a work fit for the gods!

That night Odysseus led thirty of his best warriors up a ladder into the horse's hollow stomach and pulled the big trap door shut behind them.

Odysseus's cousin, Sinon, disguised himself as a beggar and skulked in the shadows by the horse.

Then the Greeks took down the wall, packed everything into their ships, and sailed out of sight behind a nearby island.

That night the Greeks were full of new hope as they waited on the quiet waters for morning to come.

Tide dye
The Greeks used the ink from large sea snails to make a deep purple dye, or paint.

Gemstones
The Greeks probably used amethysts (am-uh-thists) for the horse's eyes.

Fine art
Gold leaf is gold beaten very thin. It is used as a rich paint.

Greek writing
The Greek alphabet was created over 2,800 years ago. The Trojans wrote and read in Greek.

Gift tokens
Gifts were often offered to the gods in thanks. Today, people still leave small tokens in church as a way of thanking God.

The next day Priam looked out from Troy's battered towers. The Greeks had vanished! On the calm sea there wasn't a ship in sight. All they could see on the plain of Troy was a mighty wooden horse.

The Trojans were overjoyed. They threw open the city gates and ran up to the strange horse. They crowded around it excitedly and read the gold writing on its side: "FOR THEIR RETURN HOME THE GREEKS OFFER THIS TO THE GODDESS ATHENA."

Sinon pushed his way through the crowd and spoke to the Trojans.

"The gods told the Greeks that they should offer Athena this gift and sail home," he lied. "But the gods said that it must be left outside Troy. Once the horse enters the city no one can ever conquer Troy!"

The Trojans were delighted and immediately began to pull the huge wooden horse towards their city.

"No!" cried Cassandra in terror. "The wooden horse is a trick!"

But no one listened to her. The Trojans rolled the giant horse through the gates of Troy.

People covered the horse in beautiful flowers. All day they drank wine and danced for joy.

"Peace has come and we have won!" they sang.

The Trojans fell asleep believing they were safe for ever.

Festive flowers
During Greek celebrations, people wore chains of roses and scattered rose petals.

Hearing voices
Helen copies perfectly other people's voices. We call this "mimicry" (mim-ick-ree) which is from the Greek word *mimikos*.

Menswear
Greek soldiers who were away from home for many years wore rings or bracelets to remind them of their loved ones.

That night the goddess Aphrodite took pity on the Trojans. She cast a spell over Helen, who left her chamber and led a sleepy Trojan soldier to the horse.

"What if there are Greeks hiding inside it?" asked Helen dreamily.

Then she called gently to each of the warriors inside the horse. Her sweet, enchanted voice sounded like their beloved wives and children.

It was almost more than the heroes could bear. Tears poured down their cheeks and they wanted to cry out to their loved ones.

Suddenly one of the men started to answer Helen's call.

Odysseus clapped his hand over the warrior's mouth so that he could not give them away.

Inside the dark belly of the wooden horse the heroes kept as silent and still as statues.

"There's no one there," yawned the Trojan soldier at last. "I'm going to bed." He trudged back to the palace, Helen following.

Meanwhile, Sinon lit a fiery beacon by the city walls. From their ships the Greeks saw the red glow in the starry night sky. It was the signal they had been waiting for.

Bright light
Beacons were lit as signals for help or as a warning. Sometimes, at night or in fog, they were lit at different points along coastlines, to guide ships past dangerous rocks.

The fall of Troy

Giant gateway
The gates of cities such as Troy were up to 8 metres (26 feet) high. Troy's main gate, which the Greeks may have stormed, was the Scaean (see-an) gate.

The night was deathly quiet as the Greek army crept up the beach to the city gates, guided by the flickering signal.

Inside the wooden horse the heroes lifted the great trap door and let down the ladder.

Odysseus led his men across the courtyard to the gates of Troy. They killed the drunken lookouts and, using all their strength, began to pull open the gates.

Outside, the rest of the Greeks helped push open the heavy doors. Then they streamed into the undefended city.

The sleeping Trojans were awakened by the noise. They cried out in terror, but they were doomed.

Look out!
Troy had tall sturdy towers near the gates, manned by lookouts. The lookouts should have seen the Greeks approaching and alerted the other soldiers to defend the city.

City riches
In ancient wars, invaders often killed all males, enslaved the females, and stole the city's treasure.

Old ruins
Ancient city ruins have been found at Troy. No one is sure which parts are from the Troy in Homer's poem.

The Greeks rushed everywhere, filled with ten years of anger. They killed every Trojan man in sight and set fire to everything they could. They beheaded King Priam and made Cassandra and Hector's wife and son their prisoners.

The Greeks dragged all the Trojan women and children to their ships.

Troy's lofty towers and high walls burnt to the ground. The palace treasures were stolen and every house was looted.

Soon the city streets were flowing with Trojan blood.

At last, Menelaus and his beautiful wife were reunited. Helen wept, "So many have died because of me!"

"But we have won you back, my treasure," Menelaus said gently. "Thanks to Odysseus and the wooden horse, we have conquered the city of Troy!"

After ten years of war, the Greek heroes set sail for home. The wind filled their ships' sails and carried them back across the rippling sea.

The gods looked down from Mount Olympus and plotted new adventures for the heroes.

Modern horse
In the modern city of Troy children can climb inside a model of the wooden horse.

Glossary

Avenge
The act of inflicting punishment on a person or people in return for harm or injury done to another party.

Beacon
(bee-con)
A fire, light, or other signal used to guide or warn ships and aircraft.

Chariot
A two-wheeled open cart that is drawn by horses. The chariot used in ancient times to carry soldiers.

Charioteer
The person who rides a chariot is called a charioteer.

Civilization
A society which has a written language, arts, science and politics. The ancient Greek civilization was one of the greatest in world history.

Immortal
An immortal is someone who never dies. The Greek gods were immortal and could give people immortality, or everlasting life.

Legend
A famous story based on true events, but mostly made up by storytellers.

Lookout
A person responsible for keeping watch against danger.

Loom
A machine for weaving wool, cottons or silk into thick or fine cloth.

Nectar
(neck-tah)
A sweet liquid in many flowers that bees make into honey. Nectar was the drink of the gods. They ate food called ambrosia, which was nectar mixed with pollen, also from flowers.

Noble
Having or showing a brave and kind character. Also, a person of high rank.

Oath
A statement in which a person swears that he or she will speak the truth or keep a promise.

Pentathlon
A contest in which athletes take part in five track and field events. These events include running races, the long jump and throwing.

Plume
A large, fluffy feather used to decorate a hat or a helmet. A Greek soldier's helmet had a plume made of horsehair, not feathers.

Prophecy
(proff-uh-see)
Something that a person says will happen in the future. In ancient Greece, even people who were not priests could make a prophecy.

Prophetess
A female who makes a prophecy.

Pyre
(pire)
A large heap or pile of wood on which a body is placed for burning in a funeral ceremony.

Revenge
The act of doing harm in return for harm or evil that has been done.

Rival
A person who competes with another for the same object. An arch-rival is a person who most wants what another has.

Sacrifice
To kill a person or animal in a ceremony because of a belief that it will please a god.

Siege
The act of surrounding a city by an enemy army that is trying to capture it.

Temple
A building where people pray to God or gods.